STAR WARS®

THE CLONE WARS™

AMBUSH

Adapted by Zachary Rau

Puffin Books • LucasBooks

PUFFIN BOOKS

Published by the Penguin Group
Penguin Books Ltd, 80 Strand, London WC2R 0RL, England
Penguin Group (USA) Inc., 375 Hudson Street, New York, New York 10014, USA
Penguin Group (Canada), 90 Eglinton Avenue East, Suite 700, Toronto, Ontario, Canada M4P 2Y3
(a division of Pearson Penguin Canada Inc.)
Penguin Ireland, 25 St Stephen's Green, Dublin 2, Ireland (a division of Penguin Books Ltd)
Penguin Group (Australia), 250 Camberwell Road, Camberwell, Victoria 3124, Australia
(a division of Pearson Australia Group Pty Ltd)
Penguin Books India Pvt Ltd, 11 Community Centre, Panchsheel Park, New Delhi – 110 017, India
Penguin Group (NZ), 67 Apollo Drive, Rosedale, North Shore 0632, New Zealand
(a division of Pearson New Zealand Ltd)
Penguin Books (South Africa) (Pty) Ltd, 24 Sturdee Avenue, Rosebank, Johannesburg 2196, South Africa

Penguin Books Ltd, Registered Offices: 80 Strand, London WC2R 0RL, England

puffinbooks.com

First published in the USA by Grosset & Dunlap, an imprint of Penguin Group (USA) Inc., 2009
Published in Great Britain in Puffin Books 2009

1

Printed in Singapore

British Library Cataloguing in Publication Data
A CIP catalogue record for this book is available from the British Library

ISBN: 978-0–141–32585–9

The Republic is at war! Supreme Chancellor Palpatine has committed thousands of troops to the war against Count Dooku's Separatist Alliance. As planets choose sides, the galaxy is divided and only the valiant efforts of the Jedi generals hold the fracturing Republic from tearing apart.

Peaceful worlds must choose sides or face the threat of invasion. Republic and Separatist armies vie for the allegiance of neutral planets.

Desperate to build a Republic supply base in the system of Toydaria, Jedi Master Yoda travels to secret negotiations on a remote neutral moon.

A lone Republic cruiser approaches Rugosa . . .

VRROOOOOOSH!

On the bridge, Clone Captain Zak hails the planet.

TOYDARIAN ROYAL DELEGATION, THIS IS THE REPUBLIC ENVOY. PLEASE RESPOND. TOYDARIAN DELEGATION, PLEASE RESPOND!

GENERAL YODA, THE TOYDARIAN'S BEACON IS ACTIVE ON THE MOON, BUT ALL OUR TRANSMISSIONS ARE BEING JAMMED.

HMMM . . .

On the surface of Rugosa, the Toydarians are having the same problem.

?!

WE'RE GETTING NO SIGNAL FROM THE REPUBLIC, YOUR HIGHNESS.

I DON'T SEE ANYTHING! IT IS NOT LIKE THE JEDI TO BE LATE.

At that moment, Count Dooku's assassin Asajj Ventress steps out of the shadows . . .

I AM ONLY A MESSENGER, MAJESTY. MY MASTER WISHES TO SPEAK WITH YOU.

Ventress produces a small holoprojector . . .

FWISH!

. . . and throws it to the ground.

KATUUNKO, GREAT KING OF TOYDARIA, FORGIVE MY INTRUSION.

An image of Count Dooku, the leader of the Separatist movement, appears in front of the Toydarian king.

I AM AWARE THAT MASTER YODA HOPES YOU WILL ALLOW THE JEDI TO BUILD A REPUBLIC BASE IN YOUR SYSTEM, IN EXCHANGE FOR PROTECTION, CORRECT?

YOUR SPIES SERVE YOU WELL, COUNT DOOKU.

I ASK, HOW CAN THE JEDI PROTECT YOU IF THEY CANNOT PROTECT THEMSELVES?

As Yoda's cruiser approaches the moon, a Banking Clan ship drops out of hyperspace and immediately opens fire on them.

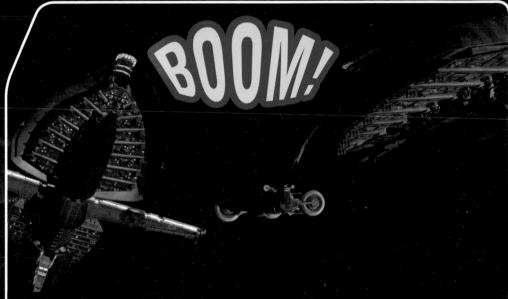

Another Banking Clan frigate drops out of hyperspace directly behind the Republic vessel.

And just like that the Republic ship is caught in a cross fire.

ALL BATTERIES RETURN FIRE!

GET US OUT OF HERE! WE'RE LOSING OUR SHIELDS!

I MUST GET YOU TO SAFETY, GENERAL —

TOO LATE IT IS. SPRUNG IS THE TRAP!

RETREAT YOU MUST! ON THE MOON BELOW IS MY MISSION. THERE I WILL GO!

QUICKLY, NOW! REACH THE PLANET'S SURFACE, WE MUST!

IN AN ESCAPE POD, SIR? THE ENEMY WILL FIRE AT ANYTHING WE LAUNCH.

THEN LAUNCH ALL OF THEM YOU WILL, HMMM?

Yoda and three clone troopers climb into an escape pod and prepare to land on the planet.

The Republic frigate launches all the ship's escape pods . . .

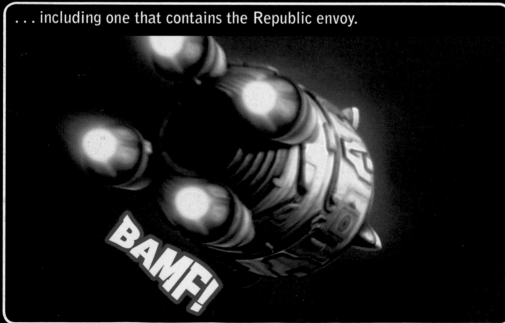

. . . including one that contains the Republic envoy.

MASTER YODA'S POWERS HAVE BEEN GREATLY EXAGGERATED.

INDEED! WHEN YOU DECIDE TO JOIN US MY APPRENTICE WILL CONTACT ME.

THAT REMAINS TO BE SEEN, COUNT.

MY LORD, MASTER YODA'S WARSHIP HAS FLED THE SYSTEM.

WHAT FURTHER EVIDENCE DO YOU REQUIRE OF THE JEDI'S WEAKNESS?

As Count Dooku's holoprojection signs off, the Toydarians notice the space battle high above.

Suddenly, King Katuunko's holoprojector begins to sound, signalling an incoming message.

THIS IS KING KATUUNKO, SPEAK!

MASTER YODA WOULD LIKE TO SPEAK WITH YOU, SIR.

Katuunko clicks on the projector and an image of Clone Lieutenant Thire appears.

A PLEASURE IT IS TO HEAR YOUR VOICE, YOUR HIGHNESS. MASTER YODA OF THE JEDI COUNCIL, THIS IS.

MASTER YODA, I THOUGHT PERHAPS COUNT DOOKU HAD FRIGHTENED YOU OFF.

DELAYED I HAVE BEEN, BUT NOT TOO FAR AWAY AM I NOW. UNAWARE I WAS, COUNT DOOKU WAS INVITED TO OUR MEETING.

THE COUNT INVITED HIMSELF. HE ASSURES ME THAT IN THIS TIME OF WAR HIS DROIDS CAN OFFER MY WORLD GREATER SECURITY THAN YOU JEDI.

HMMMPH . . . A MATTER OF DEBATE THAT IS.

YOUR MAJESTY MIGHT PREFER MORE THAN WORDS.

A familiar sound distracts the Republic envoy.

Elsewhere . . .

I AM DEPLOYING MY FORCES, MASTER.

YODA HAS MADE A GRAVE MISTAKE STRAYING THIS FAR FROM CORUSCANT.

I WILL SEE THE JEDI GETS HIS *FAIR FIGHT.*

Later, the droid army searches for Yoda and the three clones.

The droid tanks fire on the clones with no success.

CLANG! CLANG! CLANG! CLANG!

As the droid army advances . . .

CLANG! CLANG! CLANG! CLANG!

. . . the clones hide and wait to spring their trap.

CLANG! CLANG! CLANG! CLANG!

As one clone distracts the droids, the other two open fire behind the droids . . .

. . . destroying them all.

Suddenly, a squad of battle droids appears.

Elsewhere, Yoda is perched in a coral tree planning his next move!

Yoda jumps on to the back of a droid.

he droids begin shooting wildly at Yoda, who jumps from droid to droid, tricking them into destroying one another with friendly fire . . .

until only two remain.

The Master Jedi patiently waits while the droids try to figure out what to do.

The overexcited droids shoot at Yoda, who merely ducks . . .

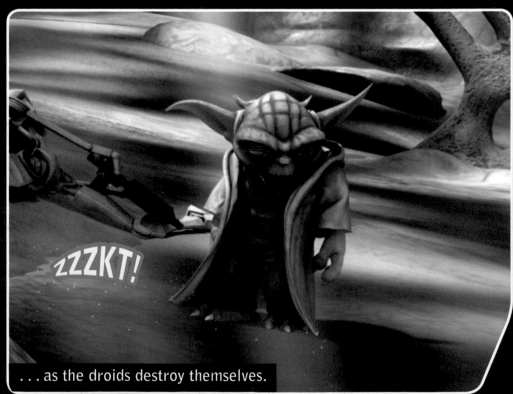

. . . as the droids destroy themselves.

THE JEDI DESTROYED OUR ADVANCE TROOPS.

MASTER YODA IS LIVING UP TO MY EXPECTATIONS.

COMMANDER, HAVE YOU PINPOINTED THE JEDI'S LOCATION?

I HOPE THE GENERAL REACHES THE RENDEZVOUS POINT.

HUFF! HUFF!

Back in the coral forest, the clones run from a squad of super battle droids.

WE'RE SURE BUYING HIM TIME!

As they retreat, Lieutenant Thire is hit by a laser blast.

LIEUTENANT, CAN YOU WALK?

YEAH, I'M OKAY.

Yoda jumps out of the forest . . .

. . . to buy the clones some time.

Clone trooper Jjeck pulls the wounded lieutenant out of the way, but they all end up pinned down behind a rock unable to escape.

Much to the surprise of his clone troopers, Yoda turns off his lightsaber and begins to meditate.

Without the guidance of the Jedi, the clones struggle to keep the droid army at bay.

Amid the frenzy of enemy fire, Yoda peacefully concentrates on the Force . . .

. . . lifting a super battle droid into the air.

The droid suddenly turns on the rest of its squad . . .

... destroying them all.

YOU FOUND US JUST IN TIME, SIR.

LEFT BEHIND, NO ONE WILL BE.

All of a sudden, the clones hear a chilling and familiar sound.

KLANK! KLANK! KLANK! KLANK!
KLANK! KLANK! KLANK! KLANK!

ROLLIES INBOUND!

Three destroyer droids roll into view.

Yoda again jumps into the fray to buy the clones time.

Realizing that they are outgunned, Yoda must make a decision.

RETREAT! COVER YOU, I WILL!

King Katuunko pulls out his holoprojector to contact the Jedi.

MASTER YODA, I HEAR YOU'RE HAVING TROUBLE WITH THE DROID ARMY!

TROUBLE? I KNOW NOTHING OF THIS TROUBLE. LOOK FORWARD TO OUR MEETING SOON, I DO.

THE JEDI WON'T ELUDE ME FOR LONG!

Filled with anger, Ventress grabs the projector . . .

CRUNCH!!!

GRRRRR!

. . . and crushes it!

Just outside the coral forest . . .

. . . Yoda finds a cave to rest in.

ARE YOU SURE WE SHOULD GO IN THERE, GENERAL? THERE'S NO WAY OUT!

NOW REST, WE MUST!

Inside the cave . . .

WE'RE LOW ON AMMO, SIR. ONLY TWO GRENADES AND ONE ROCKET FOR THE LAUNCHER.

CLICK!

AGAINST A BATTALION?! FORGET IT! WE'VE LOST!

SO CERTAIN OF DEFEAT ARE YOU, HMMM?

WITH RESPECT, GENERAL, MAYBE YOU SHOULD GO ON. LET US SLOW 'EM DOWN!

ALL AROUND US IS THAT WHICH WE NEED TO PREVAIL!

COME, SIT. YOUR HELMETS, REMOVE THEM. YOUR FACES, I WISH TO SEE.

NOT MUCH TO LOOK AT HERE, SIR. WE ALL SHARE THE SAME FACE.

DECEIVE YOU, EYES CAN. IN THE FORCE, VERY DIFFERENT EACH ONE OF YOU ARE.

THIRE, RUSH NOT INTO FIGHTS. LONG IS THE WAR. ONLY BY SURVIVING IT, WILL YOU PREVAIL.

CLONE YOU MAY BE, BUT THE FORCE RESIDES IN ALL LIFE-FORMS.

USE IT YOU CAN, TO QUIET YOUR MIND.

TANKS! IS THAT THE BEST THEY CAN THROW AT US?

RUMBLE! RUMBLE!

For the first time since arriving on Rugosa, the clones feel hopeful.

ONLY NEED ONE SHOT FOR EACH OF 'EM!

Not even the sound of an approaching tank division can dampen their spirits.

GREET THEM, I WILL!

GENERAL, YOU DON'T PLAN TO TAKE ON THAT WHOLE COLUMN BY YOURSELF?

WHOOSH!

HMMM...

IT'S THE JEDI! BLOCK HIS ESCAPE!

SUPREME LEADER, WE'VE FOUND THE JEDI!

EXCELLENT! WHERE IS HE?

HE'S JUST SITTING HERE IN FRONT OF OUR TANKS.

Yoda cuts a hole in the bottom of the tank and jumps into it.

MAKE A RUN FOR IT!

OH NO!

All is quiet until . . .

IT DOESN'T LOOK LIKE THE GENERAL NEEDS HELP TO ME!

On a nearby hill . . .

THAT'S A LOT OF SMOKE FOR A SURRENDER!

REPORT!

I THINK PERHAPS ALL THESE STORIES ABOUT THE JEDI ARE TRUE.

THE FIGHT ISN'T OVER YET, MAJESTY.

Ventress hits the communicator on her wrist and signals a fresh squad of droids.

THE GENERAL IS CUTTING 'EM UP!

WE GOT TROUBLE!

RUMBLE! RUMBLE!

Down in the ravine, Yoda continues to dismantle the tanks and droids around him, unaware of the danger headed his way.

KSSSSSHT!

BOOM!

VSSSSKT!

On the ridge above, the clones figure out a way to help the Jedi Master.

I THINK I KNOW HOW TO DEAL WITH THEM.

At that moment, Yoda notices droidekas approaching and prepares himself for a fight.

FWOOSH!

Lieutenant Thire launches a single rocket . . .

. . . aimed at an overhanging rock directly above the destroyer droids.

The rocket hits the target and . . .

. . . rains down boulder-sized rocks on to the destroyer droids . . .

. . . smashing them all.

With the battle over, Yoda meditates to conserve his energy as he waits for the clones to join him.

A birdlike neebray senses the peace and calm in Yoda . . .

. . . and lands on his finger, unafraid.

Yoda and the neebray sit together . . .

HMMMM . . .!

FWIP! FWIP! FWIP!

LEARNED SOMETHING TODAY HAVE YOU, LIEUTENANT?

. . . until the presence of the clones startles the creature and it flies off.

I THINK WE ALL DID, GENERAL.

COME. BEHIND SCHEDULE ARE WE, NOT POLITE TO BE LATE!

Back on the hill, King Katuunko relays his decision to Count Dooku.

YOUR AGENT ALSO PROMISED ME YODA WOULD GET A FAIR FIGHT.

I WILL NOT DEAL WITH THOSE WHO BREAK THEIR WORDS.

SO BE IT. PERHAPS OUR NEGOTIATIONS WILL BE MORE FRUITFUL WITH YOUR **SUCCESSOR**!

VENTRESS, KILL HIM!

Ventress ignites her lightsabers and prepares to follow her orders.

Immediately, Toydarian guards step in front of their king, determined to protect him.

Ventress easily dispatches the guards with a single Force-push.

OOOF!

UNH!

CRASH!

As Ventress prepares to strike the final blow . . .

?!

. . . Yoda uses his mastery of the Force to freeze her.

GRRR!

No matter how hard Ventress struggles, she is unable to move.

Yoda turns toward Ventress and, with a flick of the wrist, sends her sliding backwards.

STRONG YOU ARE WITH THE DARK SIDE, YOUNG ONE, BUT NOT THAT STRONG.

STILL MUCH TO LEARN YOU HAVE.

To prove his point, Yoda waves his hand . . .

. . . and Force-pulls both of Ventress's lightsabers from her hands.

Realizing she is overmatched, Ventress races to her ship . . .

. . . and makes a quick getaway.

YOUR MAJESTY, FAIL YOU, WE WILL NOT!

The Republic cruiser reenters the system as Republic forces swarm the planet to provide protection from any remaining Separatist droids.

Yoda and King Katuunko board a gunship to make plans for the Republic's base and to seal their agreement.

The end.

Bonus Adventure!
Cloak of Darkness

Viceroy Gunray captured! Senator Padmé Amidala has scored a victory against the Separatist Alliance on the remote world of Rodia by securing the arrest of diabolical confederate leader Nute Gunray.

The Jedi Council has dispatched Master Luminara Unduli and Padawan Ahsoka Tano to escort the Viceroy to Coruscant under heavy guard. Once there, he will face trial for his many war crimes.

CAPTAIN, HAVE YOU MADE CONTACT WITH THE CRUISER?

YES, GENERAL. WE'LL PATCH YOU THROUGH NOW.

JEDI CRUISER *TRANQUILITY*, THIS IS GENERAL LUMINARA UNDULI REQUESTING PERMISSION TO LAND.

YOU ARE CLEARED, GENERAL. WE AWAIT YOUR PRISONER'S ARRIVAL.

IT'S GUNRAY'S ARMY WE HAVE TO WORRY ABOUT. WE MUST BE CAUTIOUS!

HOW DOES A MONEY-GRUBBING WORM LIKE GUNRAY RATE ALL THIS SECURITY?

As the Jedi seal the Viceroy into a holding cell, the cruiser is rocked by laser blasts.

BOOM! BOOM! BOOM!

DROID FIGHTERS INCOMING! THEY'VE BROUGHT BOARDING SHIPS!

SUPER BATTLE DROIDS HAVE BREACHED OUR HULL!

Before anyone knows what has happened, the entire ship is plunged into chaos.

KZZZ! KZZZ!

THEY'RE HEADED FOR THE DETENTION LEVEL!

WE NEED REINFORCEMENTS!

COMMANDER, I'LL NEED YOUR ASSISTANCE.

AHSOKA, YOU WILL STAY HERE WITH CAPTAIN ARGYUS. GUARD THE VICEROY!

Luminara and the clones sweep the cruiser for droids . . .

KZZZZT!

KZZZZH!

KZZZZT!

. . . clearing out the ship level by level.

THAT LOOKS LIKE THE LAST OF THEM, GENERAL.

YES, COMMANDER, BUT I SENSE OUR TROUBLES ARE NOT OVER.

SOUNDS LIKE YOUR RESCUE DIDN'T WORK!

Back at the Viceroy's holding cell . . .

I – I AM READY TO DISCUSS A BARGAIN AGAIN.

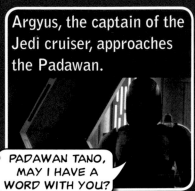

Argyus, the captain of the Jedi cruiser, approaches the Padawan.

PADAWAN TANO, MAY I HAVE A WORD WITH YOU?

CERTAINLY, CAPTAIN.

I'VE GOT THE ALL CLEAR. THE ENEMY HAS BEEN REPELLED.

AND THEIR ATTEMPT TO FREE GUNRAY HAS . . .

Ahsoka is interrupted by the sound of lightsabers cutting through reinforced steel.

Asajj Ventress jumps out of the hole and takes out the Senate guards and Captain Argyus.

IF IT ISN'T SKYWALKER'S FILTHY, OBNOXIOUS LITTLE PET.

STAND DOWN AND I'LL GIVE YOU A COOKIE.

HOW NICE OF YOU! TELL YOU WHAT . . . I'LL GIVE YOU A MERCIFUL DEATH.

The dark assassin uses her power to push past the apprentice . . .

. . . and free Gunray.

Luminara rushes in to help Ahsoka.

WHOOSH!

Using the Force . . .

. . . Ventress makes a quick escape down a turbolift shaft.

OUR ATTACKER HAS COME FOR GUNRAY. STAY HERE AND GUARD HIM. I'LL CONFRONT HER MYSELF.

I CAN'T LET HER FACE THAT LOWLIFE ALONE. WOULDN'T WE HAVE A BETTER CHANCE OF STOPPING HER IF I HELPED?

SOMETIMES BEING A GOOD SOLDIER MEANS DOING WHAT YOU THINK IS RIGHT. THAT IS WHY WE'RE SUPERIOR TO DROIDS.

With that, Ahsoka disobeys her orders and jumps down the turbolift shaft.

Suddenly, Captain Argyus turns on the two Senate guards and shoots them down.

NO, PLEASE DON'T!

OH, DO SHUT UP! COUNT DOOKU IS PAYING ME A FORTUNE TO DELIVER YOUR SLIMY CARCASS.

Using the Viceroy as a living shield, Captain Argyus heads towards the Republic frigate housed in the belly of the *Tranquility*.

Onboard the frigate, Argyus starts the launch sequence . . .

THE OUTER SHIELDS ARE STILL DOWN! THE SHIP IS STILL IN TURMOIL! WE'RE HOME FREE!

AS SUCCESSFUL A RESCUE AS ONE COULD HOPE FOR, VICEROY. I'LL BE A LEGEND FOR THIS.

YOU SEE, ASSASSIN, OUR PLAN WENT OFF WITHOUT A HITCH.

The door to the bridge opens and Ventress strides in, having evaded both Jedi.

AND I WILL, OF COURSE, MAKE SURE YOUR CONTRIBUTIONS ARE NOTED IN MY REPORT TO COUNT DOOKU.

VZZZZZZH!

I'LL TELL HIM MYSELF!

True to her nature, Ventress betrays Argyus and pierces his heart with a lightsaber.

I ALWAYS HAD A GOOD FEELING ABOUT YOU, ASSASSIN!

Later on the bridge of the *Tranquility* . . .

A COWARD VICEROY GUNRAY IS, BUT POWERFUL ALLIES HE HAS! SWIFTLY WE MUST MOVE, IF WE ARE TO RECAPTURE HIM.

AHSOKA, I'LL MEET YOU AT THE RENDEZVOUS POINT.

YES, MASTER.

MASTER LUMINARA, I GUESS THIS IS GOODBYE FOR NOW.

THANK YOU, MASTER!

FAREWELL.

The end.